SONGS
FOR LIFE

VOLUME 1 – FULL MUSIC

COMPILED BY GEOFF WEAVER
& DAVID OGDEN

RS✦M

Copyright information and acknowledgments

First published 2000.

Those who control the copyright in the music and words are identified at the foot of the first page of each item. Please note that in many cases the RSCM does not own or control the copyright in works used. Permission to reproduce any work must be sought from the copyright holder.

At the time of this printing, the addresses of the copyright controllers known to us were as follows:

Ateliers et Presses de Taizé F-71250 Taizé-Communauté France

Carlin Music Corp., London NW1 8BD UK

CopyCare Ltd, PO Box 77, Hailsham, East Sussex BN27 3EF UK

Helena Hobbs, c/o The Royal School of Church Music

Hope Publishing Company, 380 South Main Place, Carol Stream IL60188 USA

New Cadenza Music Corp./Valando Music Inc., USA

Oregon Catholic Press, 5536 NE Hassalo, Portland, Oregon 97213-3638 USA

Royal School of Church Music, Cleveland Lodge, Westhumble, Dorking, Surrey RH5 6BW UK

Scripture in Song, Kingsway's ThankYou Music, PO Box 75, Eastbourne, East Sussex BN23 6NN UK

Sovereign Lifestyle Music, PO Box 356, Leighton Buzzard, Bedfordshire LU7 8WP UK

Stainer & Bell Ltd, PO Box 110, Victoria House, 23 Gruneisen Road, Finchley, London N3 lDZ UK

WGRG (Wild Goose), Iona Community, Glasgow G51 3UU, Scotland UK

We have made every effort to identify all copyright holders and to all of them we are most grateful. We apologise if there are any errors or omissions and we will correct them in future printings.

ISBN 0-85402-104-3

Music origination by William Llewellyn.
Editorial assistance and production by Jane Hiley, Esther Jones,
William Llewellyn, Tim Rogers and Alistair Warwick.
Cover design by Jonathan Bates.
Printed in Great Britain by Caligraving Limited.

Contents

1 – 9: canons, 10 – 16: short songs, 17 – 27: songs

No.	Title	Key	VFL Level
1	Praise God, from whom all blessings flow	G	LB
2	Gloria	F	LB
3	Shalom chaverim	e	LB
4	Hosanna in excelsis	E	LB
5	Ma tovu	g	LB
6	Thumba thumba	e	LB/DB
7	Alleluia	F	DB/R
8	Jubilate Deo	C	DB/R
9	When Jesus wept	e	DB
10	Celtic alleluia	G	LB/DB
11	Halle, halle, hallelujah	G	LB/DB
12	Siyahamba	G	all levels
13	Wa wa wa emimio	F	all levels
14	Over my head	D	LB
15	Prepare ye	B♭	DB/R
16	Shut the door	A	LB
17	When I needed a neighbour	e	LB/DB
18	Jesu, Jesu fill us with your love	F	LB/DB
19	The fruits of the land	E	DB
20	The servant song	E♭	DB
21	Sizohamba naye	F	DB/R
22	The angel rolled the stone away	G	LB
23	Sing of the Lord's goodness	e	DB
24	God has chosen me	F	LB/DB
25	I, the Lord of sea and sky	G	LB/DB
26	The great southland	D	DB/R
27	By and by	G	DB/R
28	Steal away	G	DB

LB: Light Blue level   DB: Dark Blue level   R: Red level

Uppercase key signatures indicate major mode, lowercase indicate minor.
For an alphabetical index of songs, see p. 78.

SONGS FOR LIFE

Songs for Life is a resource book to accompany *Programme One* (Children's Voices) and *Programme Four* (Adult Beginners) of the RSCM's exciting new *Voice for Life* training scheme.

Within this collection you will find short songs, canons and a varied selection of songs in unison or two parts. For each song there is an indication of the appropriate *Voice for Life* level (see p. 3). This will enable choir trainers to complement training material with appropriate repertoire, which will be useful for singers as they prepare for *Voice for Life* assessments.

The short songs will be very useful as warm-ups. Many of them have simple descants, and they can easily be sung from memory. Canons provide an excellent preparation for part singing and encourage careful listening and good intonation. The songs from Africa, from the Spiritual tradition, from Australia and from the British Isles provide a varied and colourful collection. Many of them may be new to you, but all have been tried and tested to great acclaim. They may be sung in unison, but can often be sung in two or three parts, depending on your resources. Performance notes are included for each song to help you to get the best out of your choir.

When teaching canons, make sure that the melody is well known before attempting to sing in two parts, gradually building the confidence of the singers to enable them to sing in four parts. Canons are most effective when sung from memory and sung unaccompanied. You may also experiment with spatial separation between the different groups – this helps the singers to listen carefully and to establish an 'inner pulse'.

The keyboard parts are deliberately simple, and we recommend the use of instruments and percussion where appropriate. However, never teach from the keyboard; encourage the singers to read the notes, and use only your voice to demonstrate corrections and interpretation.

Most important of all, singing is fun – and here you will find a collection of songs that younger and older singers will love to sing.

Guide to levels

The following abbreviations relate these pieces to the levels in *Voice for Life: Programme One* (Children's Voices). Those using *Programme Four* (Adult Beginners) should begin with the Light Blue pieces, gradually incorporating the Dark Blue pieces; confident singers, especially those preparing to move onto *Programme Five* (Adult Intermediate) may also wish to tackle the Red pieces. For further details of the scheme see p. 79.

LB: Light Blue level

DB: Dark Blue level

R: Red level

1. Praise God, from whom all blessings flow

Words: Thomas Ken 1637-1711

TALLIS' CANON
Thomas Tallis c.1510-85

2. Gloria
Glory to God in the highest

Music: Jacques Berthier

3. Shalom chaverim
Peace, friends!

Music: Hebrew Folk Song
arranged Geoff Weaver

Sha - lom cha - ve - rim, sha - lom cha - ve - rim, sha - lom, sha-
-lom, le - hit - ra - ot, le - hit - ra - ot, sha - lom, sha - lom.

4. Hosanna in excelsis
Hosanna in the highest

Music: Jacques Berthier

Ho - san - na, ho - san - na, ho-
-san - na in ex - cel - sis. Ho - cel - sis.

5. Ma tovu

Lament

Music: Traditional
arranged Geoff Weaver

Wil - low, wil - low, Will you tell me why you weep?

How your branch - es gent - ly shi - ver In sor - row deep.

Wil - low, wil - low, Shall I tell you why I cry?

All my love is lost for - ev - er, I know not why.

6. Thumba thumba

Music: Traditional
arranged Geoff Weaver

7. Alleluia

Music: W. A. Mozart 1756-1791
arranged Geoff Weaver

8. Jubilate Deo

Rejoice in God

Music: Michael Praetorius 1571-1621

These two arrangements copyright © 2000 The Royal School of Church Music

9. When Jesus wept

Words: American Folk Hymn

Music: William Billings 1746-1800
arranged Geoff Weaver

When Je - sus wept, the fall - ing

tear, In mer - cy flowed be - yond all bound, When

Je - sus groaned a tremb - ling fear Seized

all the guilt - y world a - round.

10. Celtic alleluia

Music: Fintan O'Carroll
and Christopher Walker

11. Halle, halle, hallelujah!

Words: Traditional

Music: Caribbean
arranged Geoff Weaver

12. Siyahamba
We are marching in the light of God

Words: Traditional South African

Music: Traditional South African
arranged Geoff Weaver

Verse 2. We are living in the love of God.
Verse 3. We are moving in the power of God.

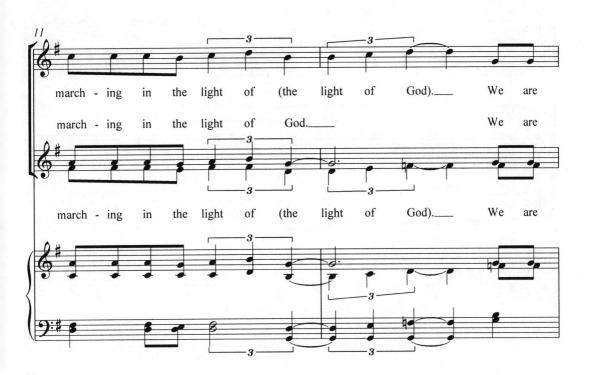

13. Wa wa wa emimimo

Come, O Holy Spirit, come

Music: Nigerian
arranged Geoff Weaver

18

A - lag - ba - ra me - ta.
Al - might - y Spi - rit, come!

E - mi - mi - mo.
Ho - ly Spi - rit.

-ra.
come!

Wa - o,   wa - o,   wa - o.
Come,__   come,__   come!__

-ra.
come!

Wa - o,   wa - o,   wa - o.
Come,__   come,__   come!__

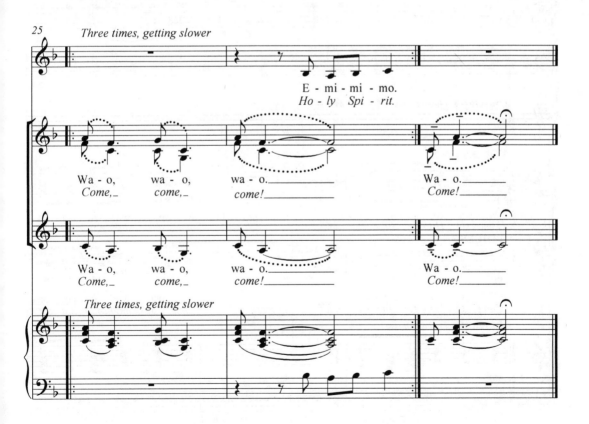

Three times, getting slower

E - mi - mi - mo.
Ho - ly Spi - rit.

Wa - o,   wa - o,   wa - o._____   Wa - o._____
Come,__   come,__   come!_____   Come!_____

Wa - o,   wa - o,   wa - o._____   Wa - o._____
Come,__   come,__   come!_____   Come!_____

Three times, getting slower

14. Over my head

Words: Traditional

Music: Traditional
arranged David Ogden

15. Prepare ye

from Godspell

Isaiah 40, 3

Music: Stephen Schwartz
arranged Christopher Walker and David Ogden

1. Solo voice.
2. All in unison.
3. Gradually add voices and instruments, getting louder each time.

16. Shut the door

Words: Traditional

Music: Traditional
arranged David Ogden

17. When I needed a neighbour

Words: Sidney Carter

Music: Sidney Carter
arranged and adapted by Nicholas Burt

I was hun-gry and thirst-y, were you there, were you there? I was

hun-gry and thirst-y, were you there? And the creed and the col-our and the

(Org. Man.)

name won't mat-ter, Were you there? I was

cold, I was na-ked, were you there, I was cold, I was na-ked, were you

there? Were you there, were you there, were____ you__

there? Were you there, were you there,

there? When I need - ed a neigh - bour, were you

were you there?_ When I need - ed a neigh - bour, were you

Org. Ped.

there, were you there? When I need - ed a neigh - bour, were you there? And the

creed and the col - our and the name won't mat - ter, Were you there?

When I need - ed a shel - ter, were you there, were you there? When I need - ed a shel - ter, were you there? And the

creed and the col - our and the name won't mat - ter, Were you there?

creed and the col - our and the name won't mat - ter, I'll be

there. And the creed and the col - our and the

I name won't mat - ter, I'll be there.

II name won't mat - ter, I'll be there.

18. Jesu, Jesu, fill us with your love

Words: Tom Colvin

Music: Ghanaian Melody
arranged Geoff Weaver

3.These are the ones we should serve,

f *but gently*

3.These are the ones we should serve, these are the ones we should

these are the ones we should love;_____ to us____ and you.____

love, all these are neigh - bours to us____ and you.____

Je - su, Je - su, fill us with your love; show us how to serve the

Je - su,____ Je - su,____ fill us with your love; show us how to serve the

neigh - bours we have from you. 4.Lov - ing puts us on our knees,

neigh - bours we have from you. 4.Ah.

serv - ing as though we were slaves; this is the way we should live___ with you.

Ah. Ah.

Je - su,___ Je - su,___ fill us with your love; show

us how to serve the neigh - bours we have from you.

19.The fruits of the land

A new Harvest song

Words: Helena Hobbs

Music: David Ogden

Flowing and joyful ♩ = 96

KEYBOARD

VOICES

Refrain   **a tempo**

You give us the sun,_ you send us the rain;_ The cy-cle of sea-sons_

turn-ing a-gain;_ Feed-ing the earth_ by the power of your hand,_ We

last time to Coda 𝄌

Verses

bring you_ the fruits of the land.__

1.God
2.Some
3.You

20. The servant song

Words: Richard Gillard

Music: Richard Gillard
Harmony by Betty Pulkingham
arranged David Ogden

21.Sizohamba naye

We are on the Lord's road

Words: Unknown

Music: Unknown
arranged Geoff Weaver

22. The angel rolled the stone away

Words: Traditional

Music: Traditional
arranged Geoff Weaver

-way. It was ear - ly Eas - ter Sun - day morn - ing,_____ the an - gel

rolled the stone a - way. 3.She -way.

4.He's re - turned from dark - ness, and He is here to stay;

echo the stone was rolled a - way.

Fear no more, my bro - thers — an - gels rolled the stone a - way, (a - way.)
sis - ters

The an - gel rolled the stone a - way, the an - gel rolled the stone a - way. It was ear - ly Eas - ter Sun - day morn - ing, _____ the an - gel rolled the stone a - way.

23. Sing of the Lord's goodness

Words: Ernest Sands

Music: Ernest Sands
Descant: Christopher Walker
Piano accompaniment by Paul Inwood

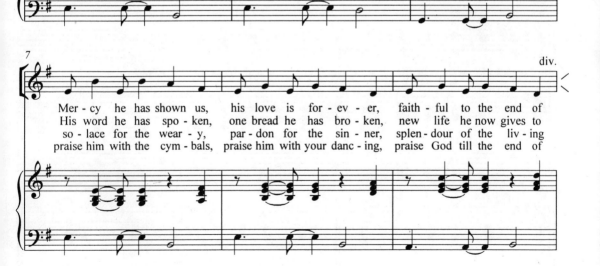

24. God has chosen me

Words: Bernadette Farrell
from Isaiah 61:1-2

Music: Bernadette Farrell
arranged Geoff Weaver

54

18

break down fear,_ yes, God's time is near,_ God's time is near,_ God's

break down fear,_ yes, God's time is near,_ God's time is near,_ God's

21

[1. 2.

time is near,_ God's time is near._

time is near,_ God's time is near._

24

[3.

rit.

2.God has
3.God is

time is near._

Ah._____

2.God has
3.God is

time is near._

Ah._____

rit.

25. I, the Lord of sea and sky

Words: Daniel L Schutte

Music: Daniel L Schutte
arranged Geoff Weaver

30

night.   I__ will go,   Lord,   if__ you
__   I   will   go,   Lord_____   if   you   lead   me.__

34

lead   me.   I'll hold   your   peo - ple   in my
__   I   will   hold   your   peo - ple   in my

37

heart._____
heart._____

Ah,_____ Ah,_____

3.I, the Lord of wind and flame, I will tend the poor and lame.

I will set a feast for them. My hand will save.

I will set a feast for them. My hand will save.

Ah,_____ Ah,_____

Fin - est bread I will pro - vide Till their hearts be sat - is - fied.

60

26. The great southland

This is our nation

Words: Geoff Bullock

Music: Geoff Bullock
arranged Geoff Weaver

coun - try___ of streams gone dry,_____ and to these

peo - ple___ We see a har - vest, and to this land. His Spi -rit

div.

I

comes._____ Ah._____

II

comes._____ This is the Great South - land___ of the

Ah._____ Ah._

Ho - ly Spi - rit, A land of red dust plains_ and sum - mer rains,_ To this

Ah._____

sun - burnt land_ we will see a flood_ and to this Great South - land_ the Spi - rit

The Spi - rit comes, the Spi - rit comes._____

comes. The Spi - rit comes._____

27. By and by

Words: Negro Spiritual

Music: Negro Spiritual
arranged Geoff Weaver

28. Steal away

Words: Spiritual

Music: Spiritual
arranged Geoff Weaver

PERFORMANCE NOTES

CANONS

1. Praise God from whom all blessings flow
With mostly stepwise movement and straightforward leaps of fourths and fifths, this is an ideal song for establishing good breath control, good intonation, a sense of line and confidence in part singing.

2. Gloria
The second phrase needs careful intonation; otherwise this sequential melody, with its swinging 6/8 rhythms, is fairly straightforward.

3. Shalom chaverim
Ensure that the initial fourth of each phrase is well tuned. Encourage the singers to take great care over the intonation of the descending phrases. As confidence builds, try singing 4-bar rather than 2-bar phrases. Pronounce 'ch' like Scottish 'loch', and 'im' as 'eem'.

4. Hosanna in excelsis
A simple and mostly stepwise melody. Try to establish 2-bar rather than 1-bar phrases.

5. Ma tovu
This needs a lovely legato line, and careful intonation on the descending final two phrases. Tuning of the tone between G and F needs care – many singers will want to sing F♯.

6. Thumba thumba
Maintain a lively two beats in a bar, and think in terms of 4-bar phrases. Tonic and dominant need to be very precisely tuned. Pronounce the first word 'Toomba'.

7. Alleluia
This needs a very strong sense of underlying pulse, and a lightness of touch – the crotchets in bar 3, for example, need to be light and detached. The third voice helps to give an underlying stability with its rhythmic precision and definition.

8. Jubilate Deo
A dance-like two in a bar helps to maintain the momentum here. Phrase carefully, and take particular care over the intonation of bars 3–4.

9. When Jesus wept
A fine, strong melody which needs great care over intonation, particularly the fourths and fifths. The long legato phrases require good breath control.

SHORT SONGS

10. Celtic alleluia 2 parts
A dance song, which needs lightly accented initial beats of the bar. When you add the descant, listen carefully to the intonation of the 3rds.

11. Halle, halle, hallelujah 2 parts
Begin this lively processional song in unison, taking care over the syncopated rhythms and the rests, before adding the descant. Finger-clicks and simple percussion will enhance the sense of freedom. You may like to start quietly and gradually build the sound and excitement.

12. Siyahamba 2 parts
This can be sung as a unison song (the middle of the three parts is the melody). The rhythms, apparently complex but in reality quite simple, need to be 'felt' rather than counted. As the other parts are added, this provides an excellent opportunity for careful listening, especially to the tuning of 3rds. Experiment with different tempi and different dynamic levels – and sing it on the move.

13. Wa wa wa emimimo 2–4 parts
This haunting call to worship is basically very simple, but as the extra voices are added, it provides an excellent opportunity to tune chords precisely and to change the mood and style as well as the tempo. Plenty of scope for imaginative treatment from the choir director!

14. Over my head 2 parts
A slow, sustained melody which needs to be established first before adding the descant. Try it unaccompanied to check the tuning between the parts.

15. Prepare ye the way of the Lord 3 parts
Start with the tune sung confidently, gradually adding the descants and instrumental parts. This song provides excellent training in rhythmic ensemble and precise intonation.

16. Shut the door Unison
Sing this very rhythmically with plenty of energy and vitality. Start quietly, getting louder each time you sing it.

SONGS

17. When I needed a neighbour 2 parts
This setting provides an excellent introduction to 2-part singing. The words need to be carefully articulated and coloured (e.g., cold, naked) and the intonation of the descending phrases need care. The final phrase, with its mixture of harmonic and melodic minor scales, requires the singers to listen very carefully.

18. Jesu, Jesu, fill us with your love 2 parts
This gentle West African prayer needs expressive melodic lines. Careful breath control is required in order to sustain 'show us how to serve the neighbours we have from you', and care must be taken to tune the thirds in the refrain. In verse 3 the upper voice will need plenty of breath support and bright vowels to maintain good intonation.

19. The fruits of the land Unison
with 2-part ending
An ideal song for Harvest or at other times of the year where the theme is God's gifts, creation or service to others. Care should be taken to practise the words of each verse in order to master the subtle changes of rhythm.

20. The servant song 2 parts
with 3-part ending
Within the beautiful simplicity of this song, it is important to establish a warm legato line, feeling 2 beats in a bar. Some of the longer phrases (e.g. the third phrase) need good breath control in order to sustain to the end of the line.

21. Sizohamba naye 2 parts
The use of a drum ostinato will add character to this exuberant South African song. You may like to imagine a procession starting in the distance and gradually drawing closer. The syncopated rhythms (e.g. bar 4) need to be precise and yet the song as a whole needs to be free and sung with a smile.

22. The angel rolled the stone away Unison
with 2 part ending
Words are very important here, and can help to create different moods (e.g. the eagerness of verse one and the sadness of verse two). The intonation of the B♮ needs care in the refrain of this gentle spiritual.

23. Sing of the Lord's goodness 2 parts
Based upon the Dave Brubeck Quartet's *Take Five*, this vibrant and syncopated number is an excellent song to close a practice or service. A hushed 'yeah' from the singers on the final chord, and light percussion accompaniment (e.g. bongos) add to the fun.

24. God has chosen me 2 parts
A joyful, syncopated and urgent song. Clear words are crucial – enjoy the dark E♭ chords.

25. I, the Lord of sea and sky 2 parts
Take care over rhythms – and in particular over the bar's rest in bar 13. Phrase according to the demands of the text (e.g. 'I will go Lord if you lead me' should be one phrase). Particular care needs to be taken over intonation of the upper notes of the descant; phrases starting on upper G need a lot of preparation and careful listening, particularly as they descend.

26. The great southland 2 parts
This wonderfully rich Australian song needs breadth and passion. The rhythms need to be relaxed – don't rush the semiquavers. Care is needed over intonation, particularly of the descant, which lies high in the voice at times. The addition of gentle percussion accompaniment would be effective.

27. By and by 2 parts
Dynamic contrasts are important here – take care to support the sound in the softer passages so that intonation is secure. Colouring the words is important (e.g., 'O hell is deep'), but much of this song needs a lightness of touch and a rhythmic crispness.

28. Steal away 2–3 parts
The intonation of the opening triad is crucial – and rhythmically there needs to be a good deal of freedom (e.g. in the triplets). The verses need to be full of drama, word-painting and mood-setting.

ALPHABETICAL INDEX

First lines are indicated in *italic text*. Page numbers in brackets refer to the melody edition of *Songs for Life* Volume 1.

Alleluia	9	(8)	Sing of the Lord's goodness	51	(42)
By and by	69	(54)	Siyahamba	14	(12)
Celtic alleluia	11	(10)	Sizohamba naye	41	(35)
Come O Holy Spirit, come	17	(15)	Steal away	74	(58)
Gloria	5	(5)	The angel rolled the stone away	46	(39)
God has chosen me	53	(46)	The fruits of the land	36	(30)
Halle, halle, hallelujah	12	(11)	The great southland	62	(50)
Hosanna in excelsis	6	(6)	The servant song	38	(32)
I, the Lord of sea and sky	56	(46)	*This is our nation*	62	(50)
Jesu, Jesu fill us with your love	31	(26)	Thumba thumba	8	(7)
Jubilate Deo	9	(8)	Wa wa wa emimimo	17	(15)
Ma tovu	7	(7)	*We are marching*	14	(12)
Over my head	20	(18)	*We are on the Lord's road*	41	(35)
Praise God, from whom all blessings flow	5	(5)	When I needed a neighbour	25	(22)
Prepare ye	22	(20)	When Jesus wept	10	(9)
Shalom chaverim	6	(6)	*Willow, willow*	7	(7)
Shut the door	24	(21)	*You give us the sun*	36	(30)

VOICE
FOR LIFE

The RSCM *Voice for Life* training scheme is now used by hundreds of choirs by thousands of singers and choir trainers worldwide. It offers a framework from childhood through developing voices into adulthood, and provides training and guidance for those who begin singing as adults.

> *Voice for Life* enables individuals to grow in confidence and ability within the choir's ongoing training and rehearsals.
>
> *Voice for Life* promotes what might be called a 'nurturing' style, offering challenges in a supportive and encouraging way (including the challenge to more experienced singers to help support newcomers settle and feel part of the choir).
>
> *Voice for Life* offers a resource that can be used by both church choirs and non-church choirs alike.

As well as developing vocal technique, the scheme encourages participating singers to develop their musical skills and understanding, explore the background of repertoire, consider their wider contribution to the choir and recognize the context of their music-making, whether Christian or secular.

Singers are given targets, to which they are led step-by-step, enabling them to chart their progress and gain confidence in their own abilities. As they complete each programme of the scheme they are entitled to wear a lapel badge or medal, giving them a sense of achievement.

Further information about the scheme is available on the web (www.rscm.com) or from RSCM Music Direct at Cleveland Lodge, Westhumble, Dorking, Surrey RH5 6BW. Tel: +44 (0)1306 872811; Fax: +44 (0)1306 887240; E-mail: musicdirect@rscm.com

RS✦M

The Royal School of Church Music is an educational charity committed to providing support and inspiration to all involved in leading and participating in Christian worship of every kind and style.

Benefits of membership include:

- Free subscription to *Church Music Quarterly*
- Liturgy planner, *Sunday by Sunday*
- Fast and reliable mail-order service
- Developing list of liturgical music publications
- Advice and guidance for affiliated churches
- New Student and Junior membership
- New programmes of education and training
- Discounted rates on quality courses

For further information about the RSCM:

The Royal School of Church Music
Cleveland Lodge, Westhumble, Dorking, Surrey RH5 6BW

General Tel: +44 (0)1306 872800
Music Direct Tel: +44 (0)1306 872811

General Fax: +44 (0)1306 887260
Music Direct Fax: +44 (0)1306 887240

E-mail: cl@rscm.com
Music Direct E-mail: musicdirect@rscm.com

Web site: www.rscm.com